Project/Process Name	
Project Facilitator	Completed Date

PROCESS IMPROVEMENT METHOD

The Process Improvement Project Workbook

Ben B Graham

www.processchart.com
www.worksimp.com
ben.graham@worksimp.com

Contents

Working With This Workbook

This is a project workbook. It provides checklists, worksheets, and forms to help you complete a successful process improvement project. It is a supplement to *The Process Improvement Project Guide*[1] that takes you through the process improvement method.

The checklists provide systematic structure to each phase of your project: project definition, data gathering, analysis, improved process development and installation. Capture details of your project in the pages of this workbook and file it away with your process maps and other project data to review with your next follow up project.

I wish you the best with your improvement work!

Ben

---

[1] Ben B. Graham, *The Process Improvement Project Guide* (Charleston: Ben B Graham, 2015).

Section 1

Checklists

Project Definition Checklist

A **N** ## Process

☐ ☐ 1. What is the process or system to be studied?
☐ ☐ 2. What is the process supposed to do?
☐ ☐ 3. What are issues or perceived problems with the process?

Project Authority

☐ ☐ 4. Who is the Project Authority whose control spans the entire process?
☐ ☐ 5. Has the Project Authority agreed to the project?

Objectives

☐ ☐ 6. Who requested the study?
☐ ☐ 7. Why is it to be studied?
☐ ☐ 8. Is there one overriding objective?
☐ ☐ 9. Are there several objectives?
☐ ☐ 10. Are the objectives in writing?
☐ ☐ 11. Are the objectives written specifically enough that we feel we can achieve them?
☐ ☐ 12. Has management agreed to these objectives in writing?

Scope

☐ ☐ 13. What are the major items involved?
☐ ☐ 14. Where in the flow of these items will we begin the study?
☐ ☐ 15. Where will we end it?
☐ ☐ 16. What areas (sections, units, departments, etc.) will be affected?
☐ ☐ 17. Have the managers and supervisors of these areas been informed?
☐ ☐ 18. Are they in agreement?

Team Member Selection

☐ ☐ 19. Have the area managers/supervisors agreed to be represented on the project team?
☐ ☐ 20. Have they agreed to an approximate number of hours per week for meetings?
☐ ☐ 21. Have representatives been chosen for each area?
☐ ☐ 22. Do the representatives have current experience?
☐ ☐ 23. Are they respected by the other people in their work areas?
☐ ☐ 24. Have they been informed?
☐ ☐ 25. Are they in agreement to participate?

Team Formation

☐ ☐ 26. Have the team members been given training in project work?
☐ ☐ 27. Have they been trained in the techniques to be used on the project?
☐ ☐ 28. Has a coordinator/facilitator been assigned?
☐ ☐ 29. Have the coordinator's duties been made clear?
☐ ☐ 30. Has a team leader been chosen?
☐ ☐ 31. Have the team leader's duties been made clear?
☐ ☐ 32. Has a team recorder been chosen?
☐ ☐ 33. Have the team recorder's duties been made clear?

Technical Assistance

☐ ☐ 34. Will this project involve any technical specialties? (i.e. electronic form design, programming, communications equipment, barcoding, imaging, retrieval systems, etc.)
☐ ☐ 35. Are appropriate technical specialists available?
☐ ☐ 36. Have they been assigned to the team?
☐ ☐ 37. Is the extent of their involvement clear and agreed upon?

Data Collection Checklist

A N

What Data and How Collected

☐ ☐ 1. Have we completed the project definition checklist?
☐ ☐ 2. Do we know what items we will be mapping?
☐ ☐ 3. Do we know where our study will start and stop?
☐ ☐ 4. Do our objectives require any special data (processing times, error rates, volumes, etc.)?
☐ ☐ 5. Will we follow an actual case or a dummy?
☐ ☐ 6. Are there any geographical problems to data collection and if so do we have a plan to meet them?
☐ ☐ 7. Do we have a schedule for fact gathering?

Notification

☐ ☐ 8. Have we cleared our visits through the chain of command?
☐ ☐ 9. Was a memo sent?
☐ ☐ 10. Have the people in the work areas been informed that we will be coming in?
☐ ☐ 11. Have the people in the work areas been told why the study is being done?
☐ ☐ 12. Are people concerned over possible job loss or job change?
☐ ☐ 13. If so have they been reassured by people with authority?
☐ ☐ 14. Have they had a chance to ask questions?
☐ ☐ 15. Are the people aware of our fact-gathering schedule?

Method Suggestions

(Review Prior to Data Gathering)

☐ ☐ 16. Gather facts at the work place.
☐ ☐ 17. Gather facts from the people who do the work.
☐ ☐ 18. Gather facts primarily from observation, not discussion.
☐ ☐ 19. Ask permission before starting.
☐ ☐ 20. Do not impose yourself.
☐ ☐ 21. Be friendly, a little idle conversation doesn't hurt.
☐ ☐ 22. Don't let the conversation stretch out.
☐ ☐ 23. Record facts quickly using symbols and abbreviations.
☐ ☐ 24. Interrupt for clarification.
☐ ☐ 25. Put the facts gathered in order while they are fresh so that they will not be forgotten. They should be charted, written out or dictated on the same day that they are gathered.
☐ ☐ 26. Do not use a recorder at the workplace.
☐ ☐ 27. Check out the facts that you have collected with the person who gave them to you.
☐ ☐ 28. Do not look for faults while collecting facts.
☐ ☐ 29. Do not solicit improvement ideas while fact gathering.
☐ ☐ 30. If ideas are volunteered, record them.
☐ ☐ 31. Show respect for the work and the people doing it.

Tools and Techniques Checklist

A	N	Facilities
☐	☐	1. Do we have a computer and printer available?
☐	☐	2. Do we have Process Mapping Software available?
☐	☐	3. Do we have adequate workspace and tools for preparing charts?
☐	☐	4. Do we have adequate space to display and work with our charts?
☐	☐	5. Do we have the forms we need?
☐	☐	6. Do people know who is to take care of what and when, where and how to do it?
☐	☐	7. Do we have a numbering system?
☐	☐	8. Do we have a labeling system?
☐	☐	9. Do we have proper storage space?

A	N	Training
☐	☐	10. Do we know which techniques we intend to use?
☐	☐	11. Do we have experience or access to experience with the chosen techniques?

A	N	Techniques
☐	☐	12. Process Charts – To analyze and improve a process in detail.
☐	☐	13. Overview Charts – To provide a process overview.
☐	☐	14. Flow Diagram – To analyze routing, backtracking, etc.
☐	☐	15. Time Line – To analyze processing time.
☐	☐	16. Work Distribution Charts – To analyze the use of time by a group of people working together in a unit.
☐	☐	17. Recurring Data Test – To determine if forms, formats, records, etc. should be combined.
☐	☐	18. Forms Analysis Test – to interview users of a form and streamline it.
☐	☐	19. Entries Test – To interview users about the entries on a form.
☐	☐	20. Handwriting Test – To design a productive form for handwriting.
☐	☐	21. Operation Chart – To analyze activities at a work place.
☐	☐	22. Operator Machine Chart – To analyze the timing of an operator or operators and a machine or machines.
☐	☐	23. Work Place Layout – To analyze a work place design.
☐	☐	24. Project Record Form – To keep track of a team's ideas and assignments.
☐	☐	25. Benefit and Cost Work Sheets – To determine benefits and costs of recommendations.
☐	☐	26. Activities Checklist – To determine activities required to install recommended changes.
☐	☐	27. Activity List – To assign installation activities.
☐	☐	28. Gantt Charts – To schedule a project.
☐	☐	29. Network Chart – To schedule the activities of a complex installation.
☐	☐	30. Responsibility Charts – To determine, in detail, how the operating people are to work together to accomplish the process.
☐	☐	31. Playscript – To document the process in narrative form, consistent with the process chart.
☐	☐	32. Annotated Forms – To show how to fill out forms.

Analysis Checklist

A N Schedule

☐ ☐ 1. Is the needed data collected and organized?
☐ ☐ 2. Have we scheduled meetings?
☐ ☐ 3. Are there conflicts, vacations, holidays, and other assignments?
☐ ☐ 4. Is the schedule cleared with management and supervision and team members?
☐ ☐ 5. Do we have a meeting room reserved?
☐ ☐ 6. Do we have an agenda?
☐ ☐ 7. Do we need any special materials or equipment for the meeting(s) and are they available?

Familiarization

☐ ☐ 8. Are the team members familiar with the maps, etc.?
☐ ☐ 9. Have all people in the affected areas, including management, had a chance to review the charts?
☐ ☐ 10. Are copies available for the team members, departments, and managers?

Meetings

☐ ☐ 11. Do team members understand the *process* objectives?
☐ ☐ 12. Are team members reminded of the project objectives?
☐ ☐ 13. Are team members (or substitutes) available?
☐ ☐ 14. Are other operating people (non-team members) needed at meetings?
☐ ☐ 15. Are the team members making an effort to feed back to and represent their areas?
☐ ☐ 16. Are meetings staying on schedule, making quick progress?
☐ ☐ 17. Are needed specialists available (i.e. computer, micrographics, communications, form design, statistical, legal, etc.)?

Analysis

☐ ☐ 18. Consider anything, no idea is too small for consideration.
☐ ☐ 19. Don't second-guess management – decide what you think is best.
☐ ☐ 20. Take one step at a time – NO SWEEPING SOLUTIONS (i.e. We'll computerize, get more people, just tell them they have to...)
☐ ☐ 21. For each step ask:
   - Can we eliminate? (most important)
   - Can we combine?
   - Can we change sequence, place or person?
   - Can we simplify?

Process Revision

☐ ☐ 22. Record ideas and assignments.
☐ ☐ 23. Are assignments being carried out?
☐ ☐ 24. Are lists of ideas available to team members?
☐ ☐ 25. Have we questioned the entire chart?
☐ ☐ 26. Choose the best ideas. (Don't present an array of alternatives to management.)
☐ ☐ 27. Remap the procedure.
☐ ☐ 28. Repeat the analysis and revision several times.
☐ ☐ 29. Check through the final revised chart. Will it work?

Proposal Preparation Checklist

A N ## Using the Process Maps

☐ ☐ 1. On the "As-Is" Chart, highlight (red) symbols to be eliminated.

☐ ☐ 2. On the "As-Is" Chart, highlight (red) symbols to be changed but not eliminated.

☐ ☐ 3. On the "To-Be" Chart, highlight (blue) newly added symbols.

☐ ☐ 4. On the "To-Be" Chart, highlight (blue) symbols changed but not eliminated.

Proposal Writing

☐ ☐ 5. List all the differences between the "As-Is" Chart and the "To-Be" Chart as short sentences. (i.e. Deliver receipts directly to accounting. Prepare one copy instead of three. Eliminate the logbook. Etc.) These are your recommendations.

☐ ☐ 6. Try to keep your proposal to one page.

☐ ☐ 7. Be sure that all recommendations are what the team believes is best for the organization, not what they think management will accept.

☐ ☐ 8. Team members must approve recommendations that will affect their work areas or they cannot be proposed.

☐ ☐ 10. After discussion, the final wording of each recommendation should be prepared by the team member whose work area is most affected by it.

☐ ☐ 11. Note recommendations that are interdependent and must be accepted or rejected as a package.

☐ ☐ 12. Include with the recommendations any changes that have already been installed during the study.

☐ ☐ 13. Estimate the benefits and costs of each recommendation. (Use the Benefits and Costs Worksheets)

☐ ☐ 14. Summarize the major benefits.

☐ ☐ 15. Write the Proposal – summary should appear first, then the recommendations, each with its benefits and costs.

☐ ☐ 16. List the recommendations in process sequence except where there is a particularly emotional or political recommendation which would be better listed last.

Distribution

☐ ☐ 17. Do not distribute the written proposal before the proposal meeting.

Benefits and Costs Checklist

A -- Attended to (yes, OK, answer(s) known, done, etc.)
N -- Not attended to (not applicable, not needed, little or no risk, etc.)

A	N	Benefits and Costs
☐	☐	1. Work out the benefits and costs separately for each recommendation.
☐	☐	2. Team members discuss each recommendation, searching for advantages and disadvantages.
☐	☐	3. Use the benefit and cost worksheets.
☐	☐	4. Contact accounting, purchasing, vendors, engineering, finance etc. as needed.
☐	☐	5. Avoid overly precise measurements.
☐	☐	6. Avoid guesswork where empirical data can be obtained, prices, work counts, distances, times, occurrence factors, etc.
☐	☐	7. State disadvantages as well as advantages. The balance should be favorable.

Benefit and Cost Categories

A	N	
☐	☐	8. Improved productivity – output/input (cost per unit)
☐	☐	9. Reduced labor cost. (Use work sheet and measurements.)
☐	☐	10. Changes in overtime pay.
☐	☐	11. Reduced material cost. (Use the work sheet and check prices.)
☐	☐	12. Equipment purchase where the dollar amounts are small. (Use the work sheet and check prices.)
☐	☐	13. Equipment purchase where the dollar amounts are large. (Get help from finance, a banker, vendors.)
☐	☐	14. Equipment rental. (Use the work sheet and check prices.)
☐	☐	15. Facilities cost. (Get help, engineering, vendors.)
☐	☐	16. Floor space savings. (Get help, engineering.)
☐	☐	17. Faster speed of processing. (Minor issues - use the work sheet. Major issues - prepare a time line.)
☐	☐	18. Error reduction. (Use the work sheet.)
☐	☐	19. Reduced paper handling. (Use the work sheet.)
☐	☐	20. Increased sales. (Get estimates from people thoroughly familiar with the market.)
☐	☐	21. Reduced credit losses.
☐	☐	22. Reduced discounts lost.
☐	☐	23. Interest income increases.
☐	☐	24. Reduced taxes.
☐	☐	25. Reduced shipping costs, demurrage, etc.
☐	☐	26. Reduced legal risk.
☐	☐	27. Improved safety.
☐	☐	28. Improved comfort.
☐	☐	29. Improved morale.
☐	☐	30. Improved flexibility.
☐	☐	31. Easier training.
☐	☐	32. Easier decision making.
☐	☐	33. Reduced maintenance problems
☐	☐	34. Smoother workflow.

Proposal Presentation Checklist

A -- Attended to (yes, OK, answer(s) known, done, etc.)
N -- Not attended to (not applicable, not needed, little or no risk, etc.)

A   N   ## Preparation
☐   ☐   1.   Is the proposal written?
☐   ☐   2.   Assign presentations to team members. (Summary – to the Team Leader, each recommendation to the team member from the area most affected by it.)
☐   ☐   3.   Insist that team members present their parts. This is important – clearly indicating the support of a person who can make it happen.
☐   ☐   4.   Rehearse and time the reading.
☐   ☐   5.   Plan that each presenter will stand up. If too nervous have them speak seated.
☐   ☐   6.   Present only what you believe is best for the organization and try to convey your belief through expression and tone of voice. (Don't act as though you don't care.)

Facilities
☐   ☐   7.   Make sure a room is scheduled.
☐   ☐   8.   Make sure the room is clean.
☐   ☐   9.   Make sure audio visual or projection equipment is set up in advance and working.
☐   ☐   10. Make sure the necessary seating is there and do not have extra chairs. (To control the seating.)
☐   ☐   11. Arrange the seating around one table.
☐   ☐   12. Have the team arrive early and take seats spread around the table to mix the team with the managers.

Preparatory Meeting with Senior Manager
☐   ☐   13. Meet ahead of time with the manager whose authority spans the full project.
☐   ☐   14. Get agreement that this manager will co-chair the meeting.
☐   ☐   15. Review the agenda, Opening – by senior manager, Reading – by team, Discussion – open, Review of each recommendation for approval – led by senior manager.
☐   ☐   16. During opening remarks the senior manager will request no discussion until the proposal reading is complete, and will tell the group how long the reading will take.
☐   ☐   17. This preparatory meeting is necessary to assure that the ownership of the project will be properly transferred to the managers to achieve decisions.

Presentation
☐   ☐   18. Distribute the written proposal at the last minute.
☐   ☐   19. Senior manager opens the meeting and reviews the agenda.
☐   ☐   20. Team reads the proposal, starting with the summary by the team leader, "the bottom line".
☐   ☐   21. Open for questions and discussion.

Wrap-up
☐   ☐   22. When the discussion winds down, or there are only a few minutes left, the senior manager begins a review of the individual recommendations.
☐   ☐   23. Each recommendation is either accepted, rejected or assigned to a manager for decision with a Time limit of one week.
☐   ☐   24. Double-check the list so that all agree on the decision for each recommendation.
☐   ☐   25. Arrange meetings to make final decisions on recommendations that were assigned.

Implementation Checklist

A N Approvals

☐ ☐ 1. Is the approval process complete?
☐ ☐ 2. Do we have agreement on precisely what is approved?
☐ ☐ 3. Adjust the final proposed process chart to reflect what is approved.

Implementation Activities

☐ ☐ 4. Prepare an Activities Check List Chart checking what is required to complete each change.
- Changes to forms.
- Changes of equipment.
- Programming required.
- Procedure changes to be written.
- Policy changes to be written.
- Changes in facilities, work places.
- Training needed.

☐ ☐ 5. List activities
- Forms: rough design, check out, proof and print or program, distribute or install, train.
- Equipment: select, order, manufacture, deliver, check out, train.
- Programming: establish requirement, write, review, rewrite, train.
- Procedures: write, check out, rewrite, train, distribute.
- Policies: write, review, rewrite, publish, distribute.
- Work area designs: design, check out, detail, engineer, check out, and revise.

☐ ☐ 6. If there are a large number of activities, arrange them in a network.

Implementation Management

☐ ☐ 7. Select an implementation coordinator. (Often the project Team Leader.)
☐ ☐ 8. Assign activities to individuals.
☐ ☐ 9. Obtain commitments with completion dates.
☐ ☐ 10. Announce the dates and name the coordinator.
☐ ☐ 11. Maintain the momentum and enthusiasm by staging visible activities.
- Hold meetings to:
  - Check out forms or formats.
  - Review drafts and final rewrites of procedures.
  - Demonstrate equipment.
  - Review drafts and final rewrites of policies.
  - Review programming changes.
  - Review work area changes.
- Make visible physical changes.
  - Facilities
  - Equipment
  - Forms and formats
- Make announcements concerning the above.

☐ ☐ 12. Get as many users and managers as possible involved in meetings.
☐ ☐ 13. Monitor progress to stay on schedule, paying daily attention to the critical path.
☐ ☐ 14. Adjust for delays as necessary, when on the critical path, with added resources, people, overtime, etc.
☐ ☐ 15. Adjust the schedule as necessary.
☐ ☐ 16. Complete all activities.

Follow-up Checklist

A   N   Wrap-up
☐ ☐   1.   Are all of the activities completed?
☐ ☐   2.   Review with users to see that everything is working.
☐ ☐   3.   Hold open houses to display new processes.

Documentation
☐ ☐   4.   Revise process chart as necessary to reflect what is actually being done.
☐ ☐   5.   Revise the summary of the recommendations to reflect what is actually being done.
☐ ☐   6.   Recalculate the costs and benefits.
☐ ☐   7.   Set up for further review of processes by making certain that documentation is current.
- Process charts
- Playscript procedures
- Responsibility charts
- Annotated forms

☐ ☐   8.   Disband the implementation effort, turning over records to the Process Library.

Publicize
☐ ☐   9.   Prepare a video.
☐ ☐   10. Publish a write up in a company newsletter.

Commend
☐ ☐   11. Awards to participants.
- Banquets
- Company jewelry
- Money, etc.

☐ ☐   12. Letters for participants.
- For their personnel files, commendations
- To the supervisors, managers.
- To the families.

☐ ☐   13. Promotions.

Section 2

Worksheets

Labor Cost Worksheet Instructions

RECOMMENDATION	Minutes Of Change	Per Transaction	OR	Per Time Period	Hours Per Year	Hourly Rate	Change Per Year
Streamline Cash Processing	75			Day	325	$24.50	$7962.50
Redesign AS-22 form to reduce errors	120			Day	520	$24.50	$12740.00
Streamline Refund Processing	30			Day	130	$24.50	$3185.00
Upgrade form scanner							
Run Daily Reports overnight							

Column	
Recommendation	List the recommendations down the left column.
Minutes of Change	Enter the minutes of change.
Per Transaction	If the minutes of change were calculated per transaction, enter the annual number of transactions.
Per Time Period	If the minutes of change were calculated per time period, enter the time period. (hour, day, month...)
Hours Per Year	If the minutes of change were calculated per transaction, multiply the minutes of change by the annual number of transactions, then divide by 60 to get hours per year.
	If the minutes of change were calculated per time period, multiply the minutes of change by the number of time periods/year (260 work days/year, 2080 work hours/year), then divide by 60 to get hours/year.
Hourly Rate	Enter the hourly rate - HR may help with this.
Change Per Year	Multiply the Hours Per Year by the Hourly Rate to get the Change Per Year.

Labor Cost Worksheet

RECOMMENDATION	Minutes Of Change	Per Transaction OR Per Time Period	Hours Per Year	Hourly Rate	Change Per Year

Material Cost Worksheet Instructions

RECOMMENDATION	Current Cost/Unit	Annual Usage	Current Cost/Year	Proposed Cost/Unit	Proposed Annual Usage	Proposed Cost/Year	Decrease or Increase
Streamline Cash Processing							
Redesign AS-22 form to reduce errors	.145	25000	$3625.00	.145	23750	$3443.75	($185.00)
Streamline Refund Processing							
Upgrade form scanner							
Run Daily Reports overnight							

Column	
Recommendation	List the recommendations down the left column.
Current Cost/Unit	Current unit cost for material.
Annual Usage	Enter the current number used per year.
Current Cost/Year	Multiply the current cost per unit by the annual usage to get the current cost per year.
Proposed Cost/Unit	Proposed annual cost for material.
Annual Usage	Enter the proposed number used per year.
Proposed Cost/Year	Multiply the proposed cost per unit by the proposed annual usage to get the proposed cost per year.
Decrease or Increase	Enter the difference between the Present Annual Cost and the Proposed Annual Cost. If the Propose d Annual Cost is lower, show the difference as a negative number.

Material Cost Worksheet

RECOMMENDATION	Current Cost/Unit	Annual Usage	Current Cost/Year	Proposed Cost/Unit	Annual Usage	Proposed Cost/Year	Decrease or Increase
Totals							

Equipment Purchase Worksheet Instructions

RECOMMENDATION	Proposed Equipment Cost	Current Equipment Resale	Cost less Resale	Expected Life Years	Annual Cost of Equipment
Streamline Cash Processing					
Redesign AS-22 form to reduce errors					
Streamline Refund Processing					
Upgrade form scanner	$14500.00	$0	$14500.00	5	$2900.00
Run Daily Reports overnight					

Column	
Recommendation	List the recommendations down the left column.
Proposed Equipment Cost	Enter the price for the new equipment.
Present Equipment Resale	Enter an estimate for the resale value of the current equipment (if any).
Cost less Resale	Enter the difference between the price of the new equipment and the resale value of the current equipment.
Expected Life Years	Enter the expected number of years the equipment will be in use.
Annual Cost of Equipment	Divide the "Cost less Resale" by the "Expected Life Years".

Equipment Purchase Worksheet

RECOMMENDATION	Proposed Equipment Cost	Current Equipment Resale	Cost less Resale	Expected Life Years	Annual Cost of Equipment
Totals					

Equipment Rental Cost Worksheet Instructions

RECOMMENDATION	Current Cost/Month	x12	Current Cost/Year	Proposed Cost/Month	x12	Proposed Cost/Year	Cost Difference
Streamline Cash Processing		x12			x12		
Redesign AS-22 form to reduce errors		x12			x12		
Streamline Refund Processing		x12			x12		
Upgrade form scanner	$0	x12	$0	$309.00	x12	$3708.00	$3708.00
Run Daily Reports overnight		x12			x12		

Column	
Recommendation	List the recommendations down the left column.
Current Cost/Month	Enter the current monthly equipment cost.
Current Cost/Year	Multiply the current monthly cost by 12 to get the current annual cost.
Proposed Cost/Month	Enter the proposed monthly equipment cost.
Proposed Cost/Year	Multiply the proposed monthly cost by 12 to get the proposed annual cost.
Cost Difference	Enter the cost difference between the current and proposed costs. You might also use this worksheet along with the Equipment Purchase Worksheet and compare the difference between buying and renting.

Equipment Rental Cost Worksheet

RECOMMENDATION	Current Cost/Month	X12	Current Cost/Year	Proposed Cost/Month	X12	Proposed Cost/Year	Annual Cost of Equipment
		X12			X12		
		X12			X12		
		X12			X12		
		X12			X12		
		X12			X12		
		X12			X12		
		X12			X12		
		X12			X12		
		X12			X12		
		X12			X12		
		X12			X12		
		X12			X12		
		X12			X12		
		X12			X12		
		X12			X12		
		X12			X12		
		X12			X12		
		X12			X12		
		X12			X12		
		X12			X12		
		X12			X12		
Totals		X12			X12		

Material Handling Worksheet Instructions

RECOMMENDATION	Current Touches	Current Occurrences per Year	Current Touches per Year	Proposed Touches	Proposed Occurrences per Year	Proposed Touches per Year	Change
Streamline Cash Processing	17	35000	595000	11	35000	385000	210000
Redesign AS-22 form to reduce errors	7	12500	87500	7	2000	14000	73500
Streamline Refund Processing	21	14000	294000	18	14000	252000	42000
Upgrade form scanner							
Run Daily Reports overnight							

Column	
Recommendation	List the recommendations down the left column.
Current Touches	Enter the current number of touches to complete the task identified by the recommendation.
Current Occurrences/Year	Enter the number of times the task is performed per year.
Current Touches Per Year	Multiply the current number of touches per task by the number of occurrences per year.
Proposed Touches	Enter the proposed number of touches to complete the task identified by the recommendation.
Proposed Occurrences/Year	Enter the number of times the task would be performed per year.
Proposed Touches Per Year	Multiply the proposed number of touches per task by the proposed number of occurrences per year.
Change	Subtract proposed touches from current touches to get change.

A touch refers to the handling of any document (paper or electronic) as a part of the process.

Material Handling Worksheet

RECOMMENDATION	Current Touches	Current Occurrences per Year	Current Touches per Year	Proposed Touches	Proposed Occurrences per Year	Proposed Touches per Year	Change
Totals							

Speed of Processing Worksheet Instructions

RECOMMENDATION	Current Delay Minutes	Proposed Delay Minutes	Change in Delay Minutes	Current Processing Minutes	Proposed Processing Minutes	Change in Processing Minutes	Total Change
Streamline Cash Processing	240	0	240	300	225	75	315
Redesign AS-22 form to reduce errors							
Streamline Refund Processing							
Upgrade form scanner							
Run Daily Reports overnight							

Column	
Recommendation	List the recommendations down the left column.
Current Delay Minutes	Estimate the amount of delay time in the current method.
Proposed Delay Minutes	Estimate the amount of delay time in the proposed method.
Change in Delay Minutes	Enter the difference in delay time between the current and proposed methods.
Current Processing Minutes	Estimate the amount of processing time in the current method.
Proposed Processing Minutes	Estimate the amount of processing time in the proposed method.
Change in Processing Minutes	Enter the difference in processing time between the current and proposed methods.
Total Change	Add the change in delay minutes and the change in processing minutes.

Be careful with this analysis. Time savings for only a part of a process (individual recommendations) may be canceled out by fixed time schedules or delays waiting for other activities to be completed.

Speed of Processing Worksheet

RECOMMENDATION	Current Delay Minutes	Proposed Delay Minutes	Change in Delay Minutes	Current Processing Minutes	Proposed Processing Minutes	Change in Processing Minutes	Total Change
Totals							

Error Reduction Worksheet Instructions

RECOMMENDATION	Number of Entries			Improved Clarity / Accuracy
	Current	Proposed	Difference	
Streamline Cash Processing				
Redesign AS-22 form to reduce errors	23	21	2	Improved form layout & instructions
Streamline Refund Processing				
Upgrade form scanner				
Run Daily Reports overnight				

Column	
Recommendation	List the recommendations down the left column.
Current Number of Entries	Enter the current number of steps where data is written or keyed.
Proposed Number of Entries	Enter the proposed number of steps where data is written or keyed.
Difference in Number of Entries	Enter the difference between the current number of entries and the proposed number of entries.
Improved Clarity / Accuracy	Enter notes that described improvements to clarity; making information more legible, easier to find, better organized, less crowded, color coded and otherwise more clear. Also note improvements to accuracy; training, automation, better instructions, tables...

Error Reduction Worksheet

RECOMMENDATION	Number of Entries			Improved Clarity / Accuracy
	Present	Proposed	Difference	
Totals				

Section 3

Forms

Project Definition Agreement Instructions

REQUEST DATE	Enter the date the form is completed.
PROJECT REQUESTOR	Enter the name and the title of the person requesting the project
Process	
PROJECT/PROCESS NAME	Enter the name of the process being studied
PROCESS OBJECTIVE	Enter what this process is supposed to do…what is the expected result?
ISSUES / PERCEIVED PROBLEMS	Enter any issues and perceived problems associated with the process.
Project	
PROJECT TYPE	Check the Project type agreed upon. **Documentation Projects** – Document and review with the team for accuracy. **Improvement Projects** – Document, review with the team for accuracy and make improvements that don't require major effort – "low-hanging fruit". **Renewal Projects** – Document and review thoroughly with the team, possibly through several iterations. Strive for the best improvements the Team can come up with. **Standardization Projects** – Document process occurring in multiple locations, review with the team to build one process that is better. **Development Projects** – Prepare a chart of a newly conceived process (new to the organization) and study it with a team of people who have the best experience available, develop a process, test it carefully, and get it approved and installed. **Maintenance Projects** – Print a previously prepared chart and review it with a team to see that it is still correct – make minor updates if needed. If the team discovers attractive opportunities, a maintenance project may turn into an improvement or a renewal project.
PROJECT OBJECTIVES	**Examples:** **Documentation Projects** – "To prepare charts and assure that they are accurate. **Improvement Projects** – "To prepare charts and assure that they are accurate, to improve features that can be changed without major development effort and to identify further improvement opportunities. **Renewal Projects** – "to improve the effectiveness and efficiency by eliminating unnecessary work, and by rearranging and streamlining tasks". Specific objectives deal with cycle time, error rate, reporting effectiveness, security, etc. **Standardization Projects** – "to chart two or more ways that a process is currently being done and develop a process that is an improvement on all of those charted." **Development Projects** – "To chart, develop and obtain approval for (enter a description of the newly conceived process to be developed)". **Maintenance Projects** – "To review and reaffirm the approved charts of the following processes (process names entered here).
PROJECT SCOPE – Start Point	Enter the point where the study will begin – Application received, order received…
PROJECT SCOPE – End Point	Enter the point where the study will end – Policy issued, order shipped…
MAJOR RECORDS / SYSTEMS INVOLVED	Enter the systems, forms and documents that drive / support the process.
DEPARTMENTS / AREAS INVOLVED	Enter the names of departments involved in the project.
TEAM MEMBERS	Enter the name and phone number / email for each Team Member assigned to the project team.
FACILITATOR	Enter the team facilitator name and phone.
Approvals	
START DATE	Enter the date the project will start.
EST. COMPLETION DATE	Enter the date the project is expected to be completed.
PROJECT FACILITATOR	Project Facilitator signs and dates.
PROCESS IMPROVEMENT MANAGER	Process improvement Manager signs and dates.
PROJECT OWNER – Project Authority	Project Owner signs and dates.

Project Definition Agreement

<table>
<tr><td rowspan="4" style="writing-mode: vertical;">Process</td><td colspan="2">REQUEST DATE   PROJECT REQUESTOR – Name & Title</td></tr>
</table>

	REQUEST DATE	PROJECT REQUESTOR – Name & Title
Process	PROJECT/PROCESS NAME	
	PROCESS OBJECTIVE – What is it supposed to do?	
	ISSUES / PERCEIVED PROBLEMS	

PROJECT TYPE

○ Documentation	○ Renewal ○ Development
○ Improvement	○ Standardization ○ Maintenance

PROJECT OBJECTIVES

PROJECT SCOPE – Start Point	PROJECT SCOPE – End Point

MAJOR RECORDS / SYSTEMS INVOLVED

DEPARTMENTS / AREAS INVOLVED	TEAM MEMBERS	Phone/email

FACILITATOR		Phone/email

START DATE	EST. COMPLETION DATE	

Project

PROJECT FACILITATOR	DATE	
PROCESS IMPROVEMENT MANAGER		DATE
PROJECT OWNER – Project Authority		DATE

Approvals

Instructions for Team Leaders

Schedule Meetings

- Be clear on meeting times and duration.
- Don't allow meetings to run over.
- Keep on the subject by using the chart(s).
- Keep project objectives in front of the team.

Familiarize Team Members with Chart(s)

- Have the person who drew the chart explain it.
- You explain the chart.
- Have one or two team members explain parts of the chart.
- Use an overview chart to highlight documents, relationships and flow.
- Make smaller charts available to team members.

Lead Improvement Sessions

- Start at the beginning.
- Work on each step – one at a time.
- Work closely with the Recorder.
  - *Make sure ideas are recorded.*
  - *Review the Recorder's list of ideas at the end of each meeting.*
  - *Make sure assignments are recorded.*
  - *Make sure each member receives a list of assignments and ideas before each meeting.*
- Strive for consensus by continually assessing ideas in terms of organizational benefits.
- Accept ideas from outside the team – but only for consideration by the team. The team retains the responsibility to recommend what they think is best.
- Post ideas on the chart.
- Make sure that ideas are tested by remapping the changes.

Pull the Project Together

- Use cost and benefit analysis to firm up individual recommendations and focus on return on investment (ROI).
- Get a final chart of the proposed process.
- Where new forms are recommended, make drafts to help work through the recommendations.
- Prepare a draft workplace layout when appropriate.

Try to Keep all Team Members Involved

Vigorously Avoid Delays

Get the Finished Chart into the Chart Library

See that Team Members get Deserved Credit

Keep the Effort on a High Plane by Continually Focusing on Organizational Benefit

Activities Checklist for Implementation Instructions

PROJECT/PROCESS Customer Order	DATE 18 July	Forms	Equipment	Training	Policies	Procedures	Programming	Facilities/Workplace
Installation Elements								
Orders direct to Shipping				✓		✓	✓	
Eliminate Journal				✓		✓		✓
Move edit to Shipping				✓		✓	✓	✓

Recommendations are represented by a step or a group of steps on your process maps.

Approved recommendations are the Installation Elements – steps added, removed and changed.

List the Installation Elements down the left column.

Place a checkmark in any of the 7 activity types that will be required for each recommendation.

Each checkmark will become a recommendation on the Activities List.

Activities Checklist for Implementation

PROJECT/PROCESS	DATE	Forms	Equipment	Training	Policies	Procedures	Programming	Facilities/Workplace
Installation Elements								
				✓				
				✓				
				✓				
				✓				
				✓				
				✓				
				✓				
				✓				
				✓				
				✓				
				✓				
				✓				
				✓				
				✓				
				✓				
				✓				
				✓				

Activities List for Implementation Instructions

Installation Activities	Project/Process Customer Order	Start Date 21 July	Finish Date 15 August
	Implementation Coordinator John	Project Coordinator Emily	
	Responsible Person	**Start Date**	**Finish Date**
Order to shipping – notification email	Andrew	21 July	21 July
Order to shipping – Update SOP	Andrew	23 July	8 August
Order to shipping – Program e-routing	Andrew	28 July	12 August

Each of the checkmarked items on the Activity Checklist is an Installation Activity.

List the Installation Activities in the left column.

Assign the person who will be responsible for seeing that each activity is completed.

Get a start date and a finish date from the person assigned to each recommendation.

Activities List for Implementation

Installation Activities	Project/Process		Start Date		Finish Date
	Implementation Coordinator			Project Coordinator	
	Responsible Person		**Start Date**		**Finish Date**